KU-425-845

White Rabbit's Colour Book

Alan Baker

TED SMART

Individual titles first published by
Larousse plc 1994

This edition produced for
The Book People Ltd,
Hall Wood Avenue,
Haydock,
St Helens WA11 9UL

Individual titles copyright © Alan Baker 1994
This edition copyright © Alan Baker 1997
All rights reserved. No part of this publication
may be reproduced, stored in a retrieval system
or transmitted by any means, electronic,
mechanical, photocopying or otherwise,
without the prior permission of the publisher.

ISBN 1-85613-334-6

Printed in Singapore

One day White Rabbit found
three big pots of paint,
red, yellow and blue.

Sunshine yellow,
she thought.
Lovely.

A quick dip
and ...

... yellow rabbit,
bright as the sun.

Now what about red,
thought Rabbit.

What's this?
Orange Rabbit?
Look. Red and yellow
together make
orange!

Time for
a wash,
thought
Rabbit.

Red on its own this time.

Splash!

Red Rabbit,
sizzling hot red.

How cool blue looks, thought Rabbit.

What's this? Purple Rabbit?
Look. Red and blue
together make purple.
I'm a very important
Royal Purple
Rabbit.

Princess
Purple
Rabbit
in the shower.

Blue will do,
thought Rabbit.

Blue Rabbit,
icy cold blue.
Brrr.

How warm
yellow looks,
thought Rabbit.

What's this?
Green Rabbit.
Look. Blue
and yellow
together make
green!

Oh dear,
no more
water.

All that's left is
a little red paint.

Now what will happen? thought Rabbit.

Hooray! Brown Rabbit. Lovely warm brown.
Blue, yellow and red together make brown.
And brown's just right for me.

Grey Rabbit's 1,2,3

1 2 3 4
5 6 7 8
9 10

One day Grey Rabbit
found some playdough.

He made one
wiggly,
squiggly

worm,

two
chattering,
nattering

toucans,

three
growling,
prowling

bears,

3

four happy, yappy

dogs,

five
freckled,
speckled

frogs,

5

six
sliding,
gliding

snakes,

6

seven
so slow

snails,

eight
rumpeting,
trumpeting

elephants,

8

nine
spotty,
dotty

bugs,

9

and ten
squeaking,
peeking

mice,

10

which left
at the end
of the day
one
weary,
bleary

rabbit fast asleep.

Black and White Rabbit's ABC

Aa

A is for apple.

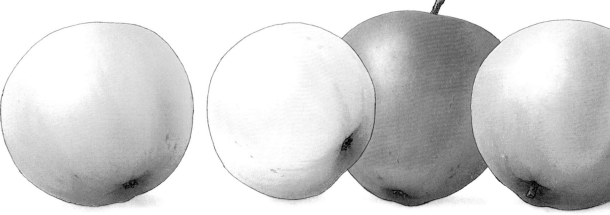

Bb

B is for box,
where Rabbit
puts the apple.

Cc

C is for crayon,
held in Rabbit's paw.

Dd

D is for drawing.

Ee

E is for easel,
to rest Rabbit's
drawing on.

Ff

F is for falling
as the apple
topples over.

Gg

G is for glue,
ooey-gooey
glue.

Hh

H is for hopping,
with a gooey paw.

Ii

I is for ink pot,
right in Rabbit's way.

Jj

J is for jumping,
but not high enough!

Kk

K is for
kicking
it over.
Whoops!

Ll

L is for leaking
all over the floor.

Mm

M is the mess,
soon mopped up.

Nn

N is for nose,
covered in ink.

Oo

O is for
opening
a new pot
of paint.

Pp

P is for the
paint,

a bright
apple
green.

Qq

Q is for
quick!
Paint
in the
drawing.

Rr

R is for runny, the paint's not thick enough.

Ss

S is for spilling as paint drips off the brush.

Tt

T is for
turning.

Uu

U is for
upside-down.

Vv

V is for very good.
Rabbit's painting
is done.

W w

W is for water
to wash
the brush.

Xx

X is for kisses
which
Rabbit
draws on his
painting.

Yy

Y is for yawning. What a hard day's work.

Zz

Z is for zzzzzzzzzz.
Rabbit's fast asleep in bed.

Brown Rabbit's Shape Book

One day a parcel arrived
for Brown Rabbit.
It had bright red triangles
on the wrapping paper.

The card was the shape of a rectangle. It said "To Brown Rabbit".

Rabbit took off the paper.
Underneath was a
square box. Rabbit
lifted the lid.

Inside was
a tube ...

... with a circle shape top.
Rabbit opened it.

Out tumbled
five flat floppy
balloons,
all different
colours.

Lovely balloons,
just waiting
to be blown up.

Rabbit blew up the red balloon.
It was big and round like a ball.

Whoosh! away it flew.

The orange balloon was oval-shaped like an egg.

Whoosh! It flew off.

The green balloon was l o n g
and sausage-shaped.
Rabbit couldn't hold it.
Whoo-whoosh!
Off it went.

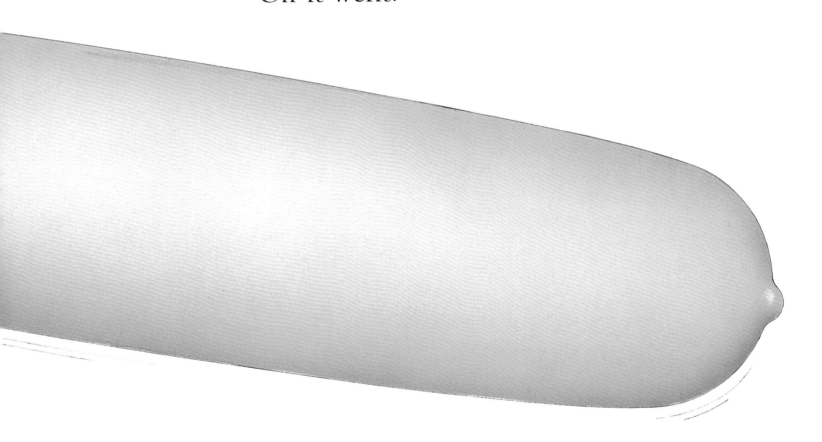

The purple balloon
was smaller and
shaped like a pear.

One more puff, thought Rabbit.
Then BANG! It burst.

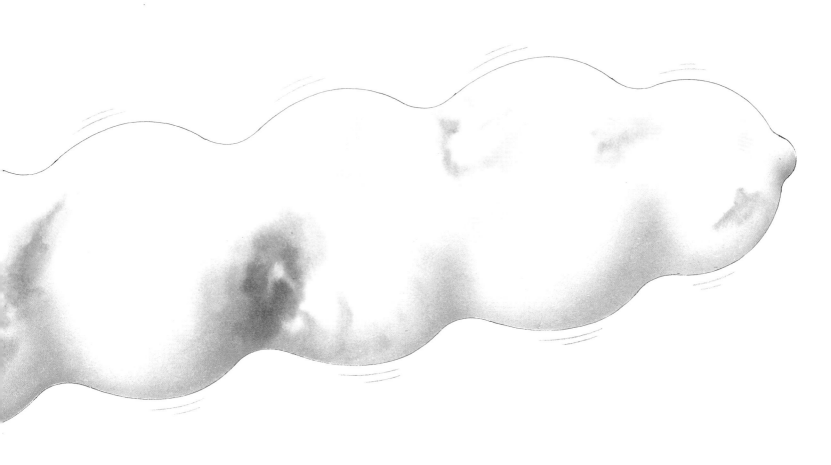

The last balloon was all colours,
l o n g and lumpy-bumpy.

Whoosh! Blast off!

Whoo ... Whoo ... Whoo-oosh!

Goodbye balloon shapes.
I'm all out of puff,
thought Rabbit.

He tidied up the balloons,
the tube, the box
and the paper.

Then rabbit-shaped Rabbit
fell fast asleep on top.